Whirlwind:
When Indians Had No Rights

A Sequel to Robert Laxalt's *Dust Devils*

By

Peter D. Laxalt

Jack Bacon & Company
Reno, Nevada
2004

Jack Bacon & Company
516 South Virginia Street
Reno, Nevada 89501

This book is dedicated to my brother, the late Robert Laxalt, author of the original *Dust Devils,* whose works about the West and his Basque culture have achieved world-wide fame. The central themes of this sequel were discussed with Bob before his untimely death, and he wanted badly to do this sequel. Unfortunately, he died before he could commence work upon it. Knowing full well that the result would have been far better if he were the author, I nevertheless hope he approves of my efforts.

I also dedicate this book to the late Richard "Dick" Broz, a prominent Seattle lawyer who was a great fan of Robert Laxalt. It was Dick's idea that *Dust Devils* deserved a sequel. Again, I hope that I have somewhat achieved his dream and seek his approval. Dick was a dear friend.

This book is totally fictional, and any resemblance to any person, living or dead, or any place or any event is unintended and coincidental.

Historians will note that I have taken considerable liberties with the description and events which occur in the book at Stewart Indian School. The history of the school is accurately set forth in JoAnn Nevers' excellent history of the Washoe, Shoshone and Paiute tribes, which I highly recommend to all readers. Factual deviations from that history were made solely for dramatic effect.

FOREWORD

…an eddy of wind scooped up a wisp of sand. In the beginning, the wisp was as thin as a pencil. Then it began to grow and take shape. Tiny sand particles whirled around, forming a vortex… Within a few minutes, the dust devil took on a funnel shape like a miniature tornado…Ira Hamilton did not consider this trick of nature a bad omen…When the dust devil had passed him, Ira pulled down his bandana, took a deep breath of clean air and reined Calico in the direction of the Hamilton homestead. It was time to get ready and be on his way to whatever awaited him there in the inscrutable desert.

Excerpt from *Dust Devils*

PROLOGUE

At the conclusion of *Dust Devils,* John D., who was white, and Black Rock Tom, who was a Paiute Indian, had become friends. Ira, the son of John D., and Thoma, the daughter of Black Rock Tom, were married. Thoma had a boy child, named John D. II in honor of his grandfather.

John D. died in Sierraville in 1915.

The little church was filled to capacity with those whose lives had been touched by the stern old man. There were many cowboys and sheepmen, some who had traveled for miles to be there, all of them looking uncomfortable in their "Sunday Best." Almost all wore jeans, some wore satin shirts, each had a bandanna tied around his neck, and while some wore their nicest Stetson hats, most wore their range hats – presenting the incongruous scene of a nicely-clothed man with a soiled hat, and in most cases, worn and dusty cowboy boots. There were no coats, not even for the pallbearers.

The cowboys and sheepmen, like most of those in attendance, didn't know when to stand or sit at the Catholic ceremony, but it didn't take long for them to bluff their way as they peeked out of the corners of their eyes at parishioners who knew what they were doing.

Father Gracian presided at the Requiem Mass. As was the tradition in those days, he was the only person to speak, and since he was an old friend of John D. over the years, he could speak well about this man before him in the simple pine casket. He did his best to lighten the proceedings, especially for the benefit of Black Rock Tom, who sat in the front row, as did Cricket, his son, and Ira and Thoma, who had their hands full trying to control baby John D. II.

One of the things Father Gracian said was that in a conversation he had with John D. not long before his death, "John D. told me with tears in his eyes that the proudest day in his life was the day that Thoma and Ira had told him that they had named their newborn child after him." Those remarks brought pride and joy to the family members, including old Black Rock Tom.

The graveside services were short, and afterwards most of the attendees gathered at a local bar to hold a belated wake in honor of John D.

Other than Black Rock Tom, Cricket, Thoma and the baby, there were no Indians at the services either at the church or at the Sierraville Cemetery. It wasn't that they were unwelcome, although some of the old cowboys and sheepmen still bore resentment about the Washoes, Paiutes and Shoshones for their attacks against whites just a few years before. At that time, the races did not mix, not even at funerals, and Indians simply did not attend funerals or burial services. It was unacceptable to do so, and were it not for the family relationship, Black Rock Tom and his family would not have been at the services of John D.

Just the opposite occurred at Tom's burial

services as had been seen at John D.'s. There was no church service at all, and other than the immediate family, there were no whites in attendance at Black Rock Tom's departure ceremony, which occurred several months after John D.'s funeral.

The burial ritual, filled with Paiute symbolism, was held in that part of the Sierraville Cemetery reserved by custom for those Indians who wanted to be buried there.

A *shaman,* much like the one who had cared for Cricket in earlier times, presided over the ceremony. To the constant low beat of tom-toms in the background, several Indian men, chanting, danced a flowing dance to the Great Spirit, all in full Indian regalia. Then in his native Paiute tongue, the *shaman* spoke about Tom and the meaning of his life and death.

Some of the young family members, one by one, then approached the gravesite, and with that great dignity and repose all Indians seem to possess, each dropped into the grave Tom's favorite rifle, fishing pole and lariat – all for Tom to have on hand for his long journey home. It was a scene filled with emotion, and most of the spectators weeped, some very loudly.

Finally, the *shaman* sprinkled dust into the grave and over the pine casket, said a few words and signaled the men to cover the grave. Each of the families then departed.

And thus, in the same year, within months of each other, two of the major forces in the Sierra region were gone, leaving behind them individual legacies, bold and adventurous, and an intertwining of the races, Paiute and white, which was uncommon in those days.

CHAPTER

I

We resume our story in 1917. Obviously, many changes have occurred since the death of the two family leaders.

Ira and Thoma had moved to the Carson City area, where Ira had a small farm within sight of his beautiful Sierra Nevada mountains. John D. II is now five years old and "all boy."

Cricket continued to live on his father's farm outside Sierraville, but he had help in the many chores. His Uncle Bill, the never-married brother of Black Rock Tom, lived in a small house on the farm and helped his nephew with the livestock and haying. The small farm in northern California was much like that of his sister and brother-in-law in Carson.

With the sturdy patriarchs of both clans now gone, the offspring had to fend for themselves in what was still very much a pioneer environment with all the benefits, and, yes, all the detriments, including racial prejudice, however cloaked and dissimulated, that environment had to offer.

It was only recently that Cricket had returned home, having been away at the Stewart Indian School in Stewart, Nevada. With the aging Black Rock Tom, Bill had been caring for the farm during his absence.

It seemed like yesterday that old Black Rock Tom had made the decision that Cricket should go to Stewart.

It was midsummer and unseasonably warm, even for the Sierra Valley. Black Rock Tom got Cricket out of the barn soon after he had read the mail.

"Sit down, son," he said in Paiute. "There is something I need to talk to you about."

Cricket took a seat on the cabin porch.

"I've done a lot of things in my life," Tom said. "Everything from being a cavalry scout, to being a trapper, then a mustanger and finally, ending up here on the farm. And most of it has gone pretty darned good. But I always wondered what I could have done with an education – even a high school degree."

And then he walked over to the window of the cabin and peered into the glass, like he was seeing into the future, and he continued: "Cricket, the Stewart Indian School is looking for some good kids. I just heard from the school, and they have some openings this fall. I've decided that you are going there – even though it will just be for a couple of years. At least you can get a high school diploma, and who knows what from there?"

Cricket was caught completely by surprise, and he protested long and loud about leaving his farm chores, about the fact that he knew no Indians at Stewart, that is was a long way to Stewart, that it would cost too much and the like. But all of his arguments fell on deaf ears. Black Rock Tom, like Jehovah, had made his decision.

And so it was that in early September, Black Rock Tom loaded up Cricket and his simple suitcase on the wagon, and the two of them left the Sierra Valley for Stewart, just south of Carson City.

CHAPTER

II

The Stewart Indian School of those days – 1911 to 1915 – was not the campus-like scene created by the Civilian Conservation Corps and its foremen in the late twenties and early thirties. In those latter days, most of the buildings were constructed out of Tahoe boulders and landscaped attractively. It gave one the feel of a college campus.

In the earlier days, when Cricket attended, the barracks for boys and girls were Spartan, cold in the winter and hot in the summer. The students themselves were mostly Nevadans or from nearby

California – Washoe, Shoshone and Paiute by tribe.

Most of the classes were held in common in a large building, with high schoolers mixed with junior high or even younger students. A pot-bellied stove was the only source of heat during the bitter winter days, and in the spring and fall, there was no ventilation to ease the heat.

There was a student candy store, where the kids could purchase sodas and chips and candy. There were the classroom building and the boys and girls dorms and the athletic gym and field.

The Superintendent, acting no doubt on orders from the dreaded Bureau of Indian Affairs, insisted that the school have military dress and schedules.

Each student wore a military coat, pants and a formal hat, the girls wearing a military-styled cardigan, white blouse and pleated skirt. All students were expected to stand *reveille* and retreat, no matter how cold or blustery or brilliantly hot.

Understandably, the dropout rate was high. Many boys and girls walked to the main highway and hitchhiked their way home, no matter how far – be it Elko or McDermitt or close-by Reno or Carson – only to be returned by irate and embarrassed parents, often bringing their charges back to Stewart by horse team because the family, living in nothing more than hogans, could afford nothing else.

The military uniforms looked nice on parade but were miserable for the students to wear – made of heavy, scratchy wool that was not warm enough in the winter but swelteringly hot in the balance of the year. More than that, they looked foolishly out of time, place and date.

Stewart had a fine marching band in those days, not that all of the students were so musically inclined. But the band uniforms were light and comfortable; you only marched on nice days, even for parades, and the Indian kids could beat the hell out of the drums and play solid trumpets. What more did you need? The band leader, an old white man, also headed up the music department, but it was clear that he loved his uniformed, sprightly marching students the most.

On two separate occasions, Cricket thought he had enough of life at Stewart and headed out to Sierraville via Carson and Reno and Portola. He was lucky to hitch rides most of the way, trundled up in the back of wagons, and a truly lucky thing it was, because each time he traveled in the dead of winter when walking any distance at all would have been difficult if not impossible.

Needless to say, Black Rock Tom did not react pleasantly to the sight of his scruffy, wet teenager arriving in late night at the family cabin. Despite his entreaties, Cricket was loaded up onto the buckboard each time, and leaving at the break of day, Tom and Cricket went all the way back to Stewart, not saying five words to each other either time. Cricket was unceremoniously dumped at his dormitory each time and walked in with his head low to greet his friends, thoroughly chastised, to face more of the military regime he despised. Being a drummer in the band and looking forward to his outdoors marching, and also boxing, at which he proved to be very talented – these were the only saving graces for a country lad at Stewart.

But he stuck it out, and in 1915, he was a proud graduate, much to Tom's delight. He went back to Sierraville, filled with pride that he was the first in his family to have a high school diploma, and he swore to himself that he would bring to his chores at the farm his newfound skills, especially in agronomy. His father, becoming old and weak, and his Uncle Bill were amazed at how much the young lad had learned at Stewart in just a few years. Now, more than ever, he truly enjoyed working at the farm, and felt that he was becoming a part of something productive.

III

His delight was short-lived, however, because it was not long before his beloved father took to his bed with what proved to be his final illness and shortly thereafter passed away. Now Cricket was the "boss of the spread." Although he made it clear to Bill that he could stay as long as he wanted, Cricket took upon himself the entire management of the operation, and a considerable period of time passed before he felt in control of the situation.

Ira and Thoma were most helpful. They not only traveled to Sierraville, always by team, to assist Cricket with as many of the chores as they could. They also rode their horses incessantly, not only at the Sierraville and Carson locations but also at the area's parades and rodeos.

Calico had died even before Black Rock Tom. And Ayrab was getting old, but he still enjoyed being dressed up for parades. The workhorse and rodeo horse that Ira mostly used was a roan named "Rowdy," a spirited horse that Ira had raised from the time he was a colt.

It was the rodeos that they loved, whether they were in Reno or at beautiful Glenbrook, Lake Tahoe, or in Carson or Gardnerville. In many ways, despite the fact that both Cricket and Ira were working hard at their farms, it was an idyllic existence.

The West in those days was like a young colt – full of enthusiasm but "all legs and no run," as his Dad used to say. It was hovering near the edge of modern achievements but was not quite ready for them, either.

Horses, wagons and trains like the old V&T were the primary modes of travel. Telephones were scarce. Automobiles were few and far between. Reno had its share, but they were out of commission more often than not, and the remarks of the passersby, of the "Get a horse!" variety, provided many a laugh. Radios were also scarce, although more and more of them were making their way into homes of the West, even in "boonie" places like Sierraville. Still the reliance for information, be it local, national or international, was upon the weekly newspaper. It came by stage from Reno to Sierraville and often was almost "old hat" by the time it was read, but that simply was the way it was.

America – all of it – was in the grips of "war fever" in 1916. Despite the efforts of most political leaders to maintain neutrality, there was growing sentiment that the United States should enter the war and defeat "Kaiser Bill" and the "Huns."

It is critical to note that at the time, Indians did not have the right to vote, either locally or nationally.

They were not granted full citizenship until 1924 with the passage of the federal Indian Rights Act. Not even that significant event caused the individual States to correct a long-standing, wrongful situation: Most of the States took the position that the Indian Rights Act made Indians wards of the national government but did not award the right to vote in State matters. That was left to the discretion of each State Legislature. Arizona, for example, did not grant Indians the right to vote in State matters (and even then by a Supreme Court decision, not the act of the State's legislature) until 1948. Nevada did not allow Indians to vote in State matters until 1945.

Cricket had learned of the deprivation of the right to vote in his Civics class at Stewart, but didn't pay much mind to it. Having the right to vote was nowhere near as important as having the right to own a farm and stock and be in business, as his father was. The right to vote was merely window dressing and didn't affect the basic position of Indians. After all, his father and Uncle Bill got along quite well without having a choice in who might be the President or a US Senator or Governor.

It was just another of the penalties that Indians were expected to pay for their past "grievances," and the fact that many of them were still housed, fed and educated at government reservations. Until they were "fully assimilated," as their teachers used to say, they could expect no more.

CHAPTER

IV

The difficult struggle for Cricket and his family began on a street corner in Loyalton in the Sierra Valley when Cricket, on his weekly shopping trip, spoke with Ben Whipple, the local butcher. As it happened, Ben was also Chairman of the local Draft Board.

"Well, Cricket," Ben said, "I expect that any day now you will be volunteering for the Armed Services."

It was late summer, 1917, and many young men from the area, even some Indians, had gone into the military, some as draftees and others as pure volunteers. Some of these men had even been home on military leave prior to their departure for Europe. Most were destined to become part of "Black Jack" Pershing's great army, later to be decimated in fierce battles in the Argonne, Chateau Thierry, Bellau Woods and even in the Maginot Line.

And there were some Indian boys, too, who came home on leave, sporting their sharpshooter medals and their spiffy military dress uniforms, soon to be exchanged for fatigues as they traveled across the US to their troop ships. There was Jimmy Cornbread and Les Eyban, Tom Iwamoto (half Japanese), Art Casey, Snooky Curley and many others.

The question hit Cricket like a shot. He had never before considered the option of entering the military. His mind had been solely focused on running his small operation, which demanded all of his energy and time.

"I haven't given it any thought, Mr. Whipple," he said truthfully. "Since my father died, all I've done is live, sleep and worry about the farm and the livestock and crops."

Whipple was irritated at the young man's response.

"Well, those things will be with you forever," said Whipple, "provided some crazy Huns haven't grabbed them all and put you in chains! It's more important that you think about serving your country, isn't it?!" He was almost shouting.

Cricket muffled his response and raising his hand in farewell, he eased on up the street. But he was troubled. Why had Mr. Whipple singled him out for pro-military comments? No, not comments, more like a tirade, he thought. Was the Draft Board going to try to conscript him if he didn't volunteer?

All the way home, as he made his way by wagon filled with supplies across the immense Sierra Valley ("Largest Alpine Valley in the World," said the big sign in Portola), he wrestled with the topic.

According to what he knew from school and his talks with other Indians, mostly at the rodeos, he did not have the right to vote, period. When he would have the right was something no one wanted to talk about.

How was it then, he pondered, that if he didn't volunteer to go fight in France, he might be conscripted? Was the one thing totally independent of the other, or was there a connection?

His worries evaporated as he and the buggy started home with feed and grain. Tomorrow was just another day, he thought. Filled with chores from sun-up until late at night.

It wasn't long, however, before he realized that Ben Whipple hadn't stopped him on the corner just to chat. A very official letter came from the Draft Board, and while it was deftly and ambiguously worded about mandatory conscription and Indian rights, it strongly urged all recipients – and Cricket had the unmistakable feeling that he was the *only* Indian to get such a letter – that they should seriously and promptly think about volunteering, and to that end, the Board had even set an appointment time for him.

Cricket had no choice but to give the matter his full attention. He talked with many other Indians, young and old, and he even traveled all the way to Carson to visit with his sister and Ira, where they talked until late in the night about the situation and the risks and dangers of non-compliance.

When Cricket awoke the next morning, as he was saddling his horse for the ride back to Sierraville, he knew what he was going to do.

At the designated time and place - to wit: mid-afternoon at the Loyalton Eagles Hall - Cricket reluctantly appeared. So as not to give the meeting more credence than it deserved, he thought, I'm just going to wear my work clothes. They can treat the whole thing as formally as they want, but I'm going to do this my way, he said to himself.

He was met by Mr. Whipple and also Mr. Aiken, the local barber, who introduced himself as an additional member of the area Draft Board. Suffice it to say that what began as a rather genteel meeting soon became a racially-bigoted spat, with Aiken in particular questioning the loyalty and patriotism of any person, any Indian, who had the "audacity to sit by the sidelines and not go into uniform." But Cricket had been forcefully and politely firm: He was not going to volunteer, and he did not feel that the Draft Board had the right to conscript him if he did not have the right to vote.

"You damned whippersnapper, you have decided all on your own that you are not going to wear the proud uniform of this country. That's what you are saying, isn't it?" shouted Aiken.

Cricket looked straight ahead in to the eyes of Whipple and Aiken and calmly repeated: "It is not a question of love of country. I love this country. But if I am not 'assimilated,' as my teachers at Stewart used to say, for voting purposes, then I am not 'assimilated' for military purposes, either."

At this, Aiken stomped out of the meeting room, shouting epithets over his shoulder as he went. Whipple was not any more kindly, saying to Cricket: "You had better think long and hard about what you are doing, son. If you fight, I can protect you. If you don't choose to wear the uniform, then I can't protect you whatsoever!" he said ominously. Then he, too, departed.

Cricket looked about the vacant room, realizing that he was on the threshold of a major development in his young life, took a deep breath and found his way to the stairs and out.

The next time Cricket rode into town, he was met at every turn with icy stares. As the old saying goes, "word travels fast in a small town," and virtually everyone had heard about the confrontation at Eagles Hall. Cool receptions and even a couple of acts of near-hostility, not only from youngsters but also from shopkeepers, were encountered.

He tried to discuss the problem with his Uncle Bill, but his uncle would hear none of it. He personally had no sympathy for Cricket's position, having lived successfully with Indian discrimination all of his life. Even Ira was not totally in support of Cricket's incipient decision.

"For Christ's sake, Crick," he said, "You don't even know for sure whether you are legally right or not. You haven't talked with anyone who knows anything about the issues."

But Cricket persisted in his belief that he might be right.

The very next time he came to Loyalton,

there were catcalls from across the street, loud talk about his being a coward, and even louder curses and shouts about his lack of patriotism. He could have sworn that one of those who was sniping at him from across the street was none other than Jimmy Cornbread, home on leave from the service. Cricket was alarmed, but remained unswerving in his convictions.

Then the second letter from the Draft Board arrived. It was blunt. It stated the Cricket had demonstrated a singular lack of respect for his country in the initial interview and demanded to know if, upon further reflection as to the gravity of his actions, he had re-thought the matter and come to a rational conclusion that, just as hundreds of others in the area, both Indian and non-Indian, he would either volunteer or accept conscription.

He was given a deadline in which to answer. It was a "short fuse," he thought, and if he made the wrong choice, the whole damned thing would go off in his hands.

His farm, his crops and his stock needed him, he knew, and he could plead for a deferment on that basis alone, just as Ira had. But Ira's circumstances were decidedly different, he knew, Ira being married, with a tender-aged child and no means of "hiring out" his chores. Cricket, aside from help from his Uncle Bill, which was not enough to sustain the operation, surely could not be expected to "go into hock" in hiring of men to run his farm while he was gone.

But, more importantly, he kept returning to his basic contention: There was something unfair about being asked to place his life on the line for his country and yet have nothing, not even the right to vote or any other way of influencing the process, to show for it.

Before long, even prior to his scheduled deadline with the Draft Board, it was obvious that Cricket had become to the townspeople and surrounding farmers and ranchers a *pariah,* a symbol of those who would be traitors to the flag, for whatsoever reason.

As the war news continued to come, as reports were received of massive injuries and death to American servicemen, the sentiment against Cricket grew even stronger. After all, they thought, he is not even a conscientious objector on religious grounds. He is just an Indian farmer who won't serve.

CHAPTER
VI

Cricket had noticed her with more than passing interest while they were both still at Stewart. He thought she was very attractive and loved her shy smile as he waited in line behind her at the school's candy shop. Then he saw her cute and athletic figure, clad in white blouse and blue shorts, as she ran P.E. and "beat the field." He was delighted and admired her – from a distance. And then suddenly, he saw her no more. She simply vanished from Stewart.

He was therefore completely surprised to see her waiting on customers in the Loyalton Feed and Supply store. She was kind, gentle and helpful to all the people she waited upon. She just sparkles, Cricket thought to himself.

When he finally got to her, she gave a quick smile of recognition. "I remember you from Stewart," she said.

And Cricket nodded affirmatively, saying: "I remember you too, but where in the world did you go?"

She then told Cricket that her mother, a Loyalton native, had contracted the dreaded pneumonia and had died. It was necessary for her to come home from Stewart to care for her father and her younger brother, Ramon, and help make ends meet.

She was named Maria, Maria Melendez, the only daughter of a Mexican man who had labored for the V&T Railroad in Washoe Valley until injuries forced his retirement. He had met his wife, Alice, on a fishing trip to the Loyalton area; they were married and had two children, first Maria and then two years later, Ramon. They had moved to Loyalton after his forced retirement.

Now Alice was gone; her father was old and infirm; Ramon had just completed high school and was working at a lumber mill, and Maria, ever cheerful despite the fact that she had returned home before gaining her high school diploma from Stewart, was still "tending" the Melendez family. Importantly, Maria's late mother, Alice, was a full-blooded Paiute. Thus both Maria and Ramon were "half-breeds."

In those days, in Loyalton and elsewhere, half-breeds were treated no differently than whites. In fact, they were more assimilated into the culture than the Indian and were treated with more fairness than the Indian.

The Melendez children were light-skinned and bore unmistakable Mexican imprint, but they also had the features and carriage of the Indian. They were superb athletes and very bright.

Their father, Manuel, was a charming man loved by everyone. It broke his heart to remove Maria from Stewart to come home to care for him and her brother after Alice's untimely death. He was pleased when circumstances allowed Maria to go into town to work part-time at the Feed and Supply store.

Cricket looked forward to his frequent trips to the store, if for no other reason than to see

Maria, whether she waited on him or not. Finally, he got up the courage to ask Maria for a date – just the two of them, whenever she could, to go riding. Maria, whose family lived on a simple farm, had her own horse, a paint, and she accepted readily.

Before they could ride together, his confrontation with Whipple had occurred, and word had quickly spread that Cricket was defiantly resisting the Draft Board, refusing to be drafted along with the other young Indians of the area. There was thus a good deal of awkwardness surrounding the ride of the couple.

Cricket met Maria on horseback just outside of Loyalton. They rode on the backroads to that point where the deep, thick forest comes down to the fields. From a hillock, they looked down upon the whole valley. The barns, old but still serviceable, jutted out from the occasional farmhouses and pastures. Irrigation ditches marked black lines around the boarders of the fields. Low-lying hedges of willow and sage separated the ownerships. A slight mist rose from the fields. All in all, it was a breathtaking sight.

The couple got off their horses, hitching them to the nearest tree trunks, and then they sat on the meadow grass, quietly surveying the majestic scene below them.

Finally, Maria broke the tension by asking Cricket: "Is it true what people are saying in town that you refuse to go into the military service?"

Cricket bit down on the piece of straw he was chewing on and said, almost inaudibly: "Well, I haven't made up my mind finally yet, but right now I don't think I am going to let them grab me."

Maria bristled at the harshness and reality of his admission. After a few minutes, she said: "It's a very serious decision you are about to make, Edgar."

He was shocked to hear the name and said in an astonished tone: "How in the heck do you know my real name?"

With her trademark shy smile, Maria responded: "I saw your name several times at Stewart on rosters, and then I also saw it in the local paper when you graduated from Stewart."

"Well, God Almighty," he exclaimed. "I haven't been called Edgar for years. I hate that name. Why don't you just call me Cricket. That's how everyone knows me."

And then they had a long discussion about

Cricket's internal struggle with his principles, all of which led him up to the present day.

"I know the answer," Maria said brightly. "Let's get married. They aren't taking married Indians, are they?"

"No joking matter, Maria," said Cricket. "Even if you were serious, which I know you aren't, that's no way to solve a problem. That's using a side door. All I know is this: I don't want to be remembered as an Indian who had no rights."

"Well, I want you to understand that neither my Dad nor my kid brother agree with you, Cricket," she said, omitting herself from the litany of dissidents. "What you decide is up to you, but a whole lot of people will be affected by your decision."

After a pause, Maria continued: "Why don't you see a lawyer about where you stand? I know a good one in Susanville who helped us a lot when Mom died. I know I can get you right in to see him, and he's very inexpensive. He may not charge us at all."

Cricket, forced to the wall, said: "Okay, Maria, but only if you will go with me. I won't get you in the middle of your father and brother, either. Let's go at some time when you are planning to be in Susanville anyway. I'll just meet you there."

And so it was that the two of them met in Susanville and went to the law offices of Enzo Panicaro, the attorney who had assisted the Melendez family. The offices were on the second floor of the old bank building, down a poorly-lit and narrow hallway.

The meeting was a disaster.

Once he heard the story of the incipient battle of Cricket with the officials and townspeople of Loyalton, Panicaro wanted no part of the matter. And he wasn't kindly about it, either.

"You are going to end up in jail, young man!" he sternly lectured. "By God, if you can't serve your country, then I sure as hell won't serve you!" he shouted. And then, showing no gentlemanly courtesy whatsoever, he led them quite summarily to his office door and literally forced them out into the hallway.

Once he and Maria had reached the street, Cricket said to Maria: "That's the last damned lawyer I talk to about this thing." He said. "No white man, and especially no white lawyer, is ever going to understand what this is all about."

Maria said nothing. Instead, she affectionately kissed Cricket on the cheek and went to her wagon for the lonely ride back to her home, where she faced an unwell father and a kid brother who was "feeling his oats" – as she would soon know quite personally.

The mission had failed, but there was much more on the horizon.

CHAPTER

VII

Was it the military thing at Stewart? Is that what set you off?" asked Ira, who had ridden all the way up to Sierraville to talk to his brother-in-law, who actually was more like a brother than anyone he knew. As quickly as he entered the cabin, Cricket knew that this was not going to be a pleasant conversation. Ira was inflamed at the precarious position in which Cricket had placed the entire family, including Maria, who obviously was deeply involved in Cricket's life.

"Hell, no!" replied Cricket. "Stewart has

nothing to do with it."

"Well are you some kind of backwoods war expert or something like that?" Ira taunted.

"You know I'm not, Ira," said Cricket. "I don't even know if this country should have gone into the damned war or not. It's not that."

"Tell me what it is then, buddy, and you'd better hurry. You have all of us in a pickle right now."

"I just don't think it's right or fair that I have to put on a uniform and go fight the Huns or anyone else when this country doesn't even think enough of me to let me vote! It just isn't fair," he blurted out.

And Ira, upon reflection, had to agree. It wasn't fair at all. Granted, it had not been all that long since the last Indian Wars around the turn of the century, and there were still a number of renegade Indians rustling cattle and horses. And the inability of Indians to hold their liquor was a well-advertised and completely exaggerated story. But the Indians as a race and through certain individuals had made great progress in all other areas. Hadn't Cricket himself successfully graduated from Stewart? Didn't he have a farm so that he was self-sustaining? And other than this flap, he had always been the upstanding, law-abiding son that his father had wanted. These things rolled around in Ira's mind as he pensively sipped his coffee.

"Tell me, Ira," said Cricket. "Can Thoma vote when she reaches twenty-one?"

"Absolutely, " Ira replied. "When she married me, she became eligible to vote just like any other person, provided she is twenty-one."

"Well, is it right that you and she can vote and I can't? What the hell makes you better than me?"

"It's just the way it is, Crick," said Ira who, though stung by Cricket's personal attack, tried his best to stay calm. "But before you do anything drastic, pard, you had damned well better give some thought as to what is going to happen to you and your family if you definitely decide not to serve. I don't especially want my wife and my kid and me charged with aiding a draft-dodger!"

"I'm no draft-dodger!" Cricket shouted. "A dodger has the right to vote, doesn't he? Hell, he's further ahead than I am. Ira, if you and I both went into uniform, there would be a big difference, wouldn't there? You would be serving as a full-fledged citizen of the United States, but I wouldn't. Hell, I'd be like a mercenary – a hired gun."

Seeing that he was getting nowhere fast, Ira decided to get off the topic. "Well, let's think about it, Cricket, and talk again in a few days. But please, please, don't yack about this in public – and watch your back, wherever you go!!"

And they parted, Ira going back to Carson and Cricket staying at the cabin. Each was troubled that things had gotten out of hand, and that they had come near blows in this most heated conversation of their lives. Plainly, Cricket was going to have to let the Draft Board know his position soon.

VIII

It was spring in 1918 but it was bitter cold. The skies were leaden and the wind was blustery. It wouldn't have surprised Cricket if the rain turned to sleet or snow.

And then, much to his chagrin, Cricket realized he had forgotten to pick up the grain and oats – badly needed for the stock. It was already late in the day, but he had no choice but to travel into Loyalton to the feed store.

He picked up and loaded the feed into his wagon, not speaking at all to the people in the shop or town. Maria had already left the store for her farm. It was nearly dark when he finally left.

This was going to be one of those late days, he thought as he wended his way over the back roads towards his farm.

It all happened so suddenly that he didn't realize what was going on. In darkness now, near the junction of the farm roads, he was surrounded by four masked men on horseback. They ordered him off the rig and down to the ground, and then they dismounted. Not saying a single word by way of warning, a rain of fists and boots hit Cricket as each of the men got him down on the ground and continued from all directions to pelt him with blows and kicks.

He lay on the ground, moaning, bleeding from cuts on his face, neck and legs, his stomach aching from the kicks, very nearly losing consciousness.

Then they administered the final blow in the attack: They painted his wagon with a yellow paint brush and even put a few swipes on his wagon horse.

Then, and only then, did they depart, leaving Cricket dazed and bleeding near the irrigation ditch. It took him a good hour to get back onto the wagon and slowly make his way to the ranch. He staggered to the front door of the cabin, and good Uncle Bill, who had worried about Cricket for some time, tended to his wounds.

The following morning, although the skies were still gray and threatening, Cricket painfully made his way into the horse barn, where Bill had put his wagon and horse after tending to him. It was a cruel blow to see what he saw in the light of day: A buckboard splashed over with yellow paint and an aged team horse stained with yellow stripes like a zebra. It was sickening. He had no choice but to go to Carson to see Ira and Thoma.

Wracked with pain and hurt over all his body, he nevertheless mounted his horse and went to Carson.

As he rode, he thought: Maria had told Cricket about Ramon's new boots. Apparently, Ramon had saved his money working at the lumber mill until he could go down to Reno to Parker's, a favorite shopping store of cowboys and sheepherders and many other people. There he was waited on by Abe Melinkoff, who was tremendously popular with the "trade". With Abe's jovial and expert assistance, Ramon selected an expensive pair of cowboy boots, so fine that he couldn't resist wearing them home, his old boots tossed into a brown paper bag. Maria said he wore those new boots night and day.

That was the tip-off for Cricket. He remembered distinctly, even though the light was dim, seeing new cowboy boots on one of the men as he tumbled to the dust under the onslaught of his attackers.

There could be no mistake about it: Ramon, whom he had seen but never met, was one of the group of rowdies who had assaulted him. And Ramon wasn't a bystander, either. He was one of the leaders, kicking Cricket viciously when Cricket lay in the dirt. He also was a "painter" of Cricket's horse and wagon.

Until he first shared with Ira and Thoma the fact of the assault, he could not tell Maria of his now-firm suspicions about Ramon.

Ira and Thoma both agreed that Cricket should tell Maria about the matter at the earliest possible moment. It was a difficult thing for Cricket to do, and Ira and Thoma, sensing that Cricket truly loved Maria, recognized that fact. But they couldn't let Cricket fester about this critical aspect of his relationship with the Melendez family.

Maria's immediate reaction to Cricket's revelation to her was one of total disbelief. In fact, she was angry that her brother would even be suspected of such a thing. But then, on reflection, she cautiously reconstructed the entire scenario and came around to believe. Her father would die on the spot if he knew about this, she thought, so I can never tell him.

"But in my own way," she swore to herself, "I'll make certain that Ramon knows that I know, and he'll never be part of such a thing again."

And Maria was true to her word, as we shall soon learn.

IX

Crick, this has gone too damned far," said Ira to his close friend. "You're not safe and now you know it. Next time those belligerent bastards are going to set fire to your barn or your home – or maybe they will shoot you. We just can't trust them."

Cricket tried to sip coffee through his puffy lips. He could barely focus on Ira and Thoma. "What do you suggest?" he finally mumbled.

Ira had obviously given the matter a lot of thought. He proceeded to speak as though he were a teacher. "First of all, I think you have got to stay with me at my home until we do a few things. Bill can take care of your farm. I'll get word to him, but I'm sure he expects it."

Ira then paced across the kitchen, continuing his oration: "We are in a very complex legal situation, I agree with you. If you stay true to your principles, you can't go into the army – no matter what! If you are dead-ass wrong, then we should know it now – not later. It won't do any good to go to the federal building in Reno. They will treat you like scum, like an unpatriotic malingerer, and then toss it all off with a they-asked-for-it attitude. So I say that we should hire a lawyer, a damned good one!!"

Despite his miserable experience in Susanville with the irascible Enzo Panicaro, Cricket for the first time since the beating actually showed some spark.

"Who is going to pay for such a lawyer?" he asked.

"Well, I will," said Ira, "but I don't think he will charge all that much. I'm thinking we should get a well-respected man who knew your father and mine. That would be Bill Kearney in Reno. He's mainly a water attorney, but he has an excellent reputation in all fields. What do you say?"

"I'm all for it, Ira," said Cricket, "but whatever the charges are, I'll want to pay it. May take me some time, but I'll pay it."

"Let's get into his office first," said Ira, "and then we can decide about cost."

And so it was, while Cricket was still staying at Thoma and Ira's home in Carson, that the two of them, now truly brothers in blood, took the old V&T into Reno and headed for the offices of William J. Kearney, Attorney at Law, where they were given an appointment well ahead of others who were waiting.

Kearney was known as the best water rights lawyer in the West, if not the country. Twice he had been selected by Governor Boyle to straighten out Nevada's tangled water affairs. And there is no question about it: Water was his forte. But "Big Bill" had a wide panoply of interests and was decidedly competent in other areas of the law.

When he met the young men, both were impressed with the fact that he was so large and so patrician in appearance. He was an impressive man with unruly gray hair who wore a three-piece suit uncomfortably. It wasn't long before Ira and Cricket were made to feel at home by this illustrious man.

Ira served as spokesman and related the story of Cricket's dilemma as well as he could. He spared no details in describing the vindictive beating given to Cricket just a few days before, urging Cricket to lift his sleeves to show the wounds and then having him lift his shirt to show the kick marks to the abdomen.

Kearney leaned back in his chair while Ira spoke. He had his hands together, as if in prayer, and then pressed them against his mouth. There was an ominous silence in the room after Ira had spoken his piece.

Finally, Kearney said: "I think I'd like to help you on this, Cricket. It's the least I can do for their sons after everything that Black Rock Tom and John D. Hamilton did for me as a youngster learning the ropes on the open range."

Both young men smiled at that.

"It just doesn't seem right to me that you are being faced with involuntary conscription, put into uniform, possibly facing death – and yet you don't even have the right to vote, which I have always felt was the essence of citizenship. I must tell you that I don't know the law in the area, but I'll soon get up to speed. The two essential elements I know are correct: You can't vote and yet you face involuntary conscription. That's enough for me to get started. But before we do anything concrete, I first want to talk to the U.S. Attorney here in Reno and also the U.S. Attorney in Sacramento. This is a California matter, you know. I want to see how the wind is blowing with these gentlemen. One of them will have the leading role for the feds if there is going to be an indictment."

"Sounds good to me," said Ira, and then added: "But what do we do about your fee and costs?"

"We can talk about that later, son," said Kearney. "For now I want to send a letter to that Draft Board, couched in language just as ambiguous as theirs, saying that we have been retained and are researching the questions surrounding their authority and communications."

And standing with his hand outstretched in turn to the young men, he bid them adieu.

Quite a difference from Susanville, Cricket thought to himself. "I can hardly wait to tell Maria all about this."

CHAPTER

X

That afternoon Kearney posted a strong letter to the Draft Board castigating it for having unleashed an onslaught of prejudice which may well have caused a severe beating to a young Indian.

There was no way Cricket could return home undisguised to pick up some incidentals for his stay in Carson. Instead, Ira gave him a rain slicker with a tall collar; he put on a baseball cap and running shoes.

Traveling by night, he made it safely to the cabin, where Bill was anxious to hear all about the trip. Cricket explained to him that he must be gone for a certain period of time awaiting developments as Kearney played out his strategy. He asked Bill to take care of the farm while he was away, which Bill was more than happy to do. He felt nervous having Cricket at the farm or anywhere near town, fearing that the town ruffians might again try to beat up the young Indian.

Cricket asked Maria to come at night to the cabin. When she got there, Cricket told her all about the meeting with Kearney, the reason for the disguise, the plan to go back again to Carson. Maria understood completely.

She told him that her father sensed her relationship with Cricket, and that he did not protest the situation. Manuel merely said: "Sure hope that boy knows what he's doing."

When she got home, she planned to talk with Ramon. This would be a good time to let him know that I know, she thought to herself. But first things first. She gave Edgar, as she insisted on calling him, a big smooch while Uncle Bill discreetly turned his back. Then she was off.

And Cricket, too, left the cabin and made it safely back to Carson.

He helped Ira and Thoma as much as he could with chores around the farm, but the days weighed heavily on his shoulders.

They had a daily newspaper in Carson, and it was even delivered to Ira's mailbox. Each and every day, Cricket would pore through the paper looking for news about the European conflict and casualties. Several times he read accounts of area youngsters who had been killed or wounded in great battles. This was especially unsettling to him, but he constantly returned to the proposition that these men were citizen volunteers or draftees with the right to vote, not like him, living in near-seclusion away from his hearth and home.

He enjoyed immensely the personal notes he received from Maria, who wrote more often than he expected, always spreading her unique sunshine into his life.

In mid-summer, after what seemed like an eternity, Kearney got in touch with him and asked Ira and him to come to the Reno office, which they did immediately.

Once there, Kearney informed them that much had happened since their last communications. Kearney had indeed met with the two US

Attorneys, warning them that this whole situation was a powder keg and must be handled carefully. He reminded them that while Cricket was alone at the present time in standing up for his rights, there were thousands and thousands of Indians like him who were ready to do the same thing.

Unfortunately, while the U.S. Attorney in Nevada was relatively pacifistic and willing to let the matter be until some definitive guidance came down from Washington, the US Attorney in Sacramento would have none of it.

He had pointed out to Kearney that the Congressional act which had instituted the draft for the WW I conflict was very broad in nature, acting much like a vacuum in sweeping up any able-bodied man to serve. It contained no exceptions, he insisted, for Indians of the frame of mind of Cricket. Further than that, he felt that the Draft Board ought to conscript Cricket immediately and if Cricket refused to obey, he should be indicted and incarcerated, to face the consequences as meted out by a federal jury.

Kearney then pointed to a stack of documents on the corner of his desk, "I want to beat that guy to the punch." He said. "These papers are in the form of a complaint filed by Cricket asking the Federal Court in Sacramento to hear the matter, and in the meanwhile, freezing the Draft Board and anyone else pressuring you right in their tracks, Cricket."

So finally it had come to this, Cricket thought. But what the hell, at least it is going to be flushed out in the open and decided.

He said to Ira: "I think I ought to go ahead with this, Ira. I can't keep everyone in limbo any longer. What do you say?"

Ira nodded affirmatively without hesitation, so Cricket signed the documents, to be filed immediately in Sacramento, exactly as he was instructed to do.

"You had better continue to lie low, Cricket," advised Kearney. "There is a certain amount of risk to you in letting the world know that you are opposing your draft, whatever good reasons you may have. A word to the wise should be sufficient."

The papers were filed on schedule, arousing the ire not only of Ben Whipple and Aiken and the other members of the Board in Loyalton, but most especially that of the US Attorney in

Sacramento, who filed a withering response to Kearney's documents. After considerable delays, as the Federal Court juggled its calendar to meet pressing needs, it finally set the matter for a preliminary hearing on November 12, 1918.

When the first of November had arrived, Kearney was ready; Cricket was ready; Ira and Thoma were ready.

Then, as we all know, Armistice was declared at the "eleventh hour on the eleventh day of the eleventh month" - November 11, 1918 - and the war was over!

Bill Kearney immediately got in touch with the ruffled U.S. Attorney in Sacramento, and they agreed to stipulate for a dismissal with prejudice of all pending matters. In a matter of minutes, what would have been a national precedent-setting case was put on the far back burner - forever.

"It's too bad in a way, Cricket," said Mr. Kearney. "We were completely ready for the feds, and I know you were, too. And I think we would have won, if not in Sacramento, then in San Francisco and if not there, back in Washington. I was of a frame of mind to take it all the way. But now the whole question is moot. President Wilson ordered termination of the draft, and Congress has dismissed all the Boards, including the one in Loyalton. So big stickers like Whipple and Aiken, who are nothing more than bigots parading as officials, are out of a job – permanently."

"I am sorry that we didn't go to court, too," said Cricket. "I really felt that there was no authority to conscript me when I didn't have the basic right to vote. I'm still upset every time I think about it, and I hope that someone, somewhere will finally correct the situation."

Then there was an awkward pause as Kearney stood to bid farewell to the young men.

"As for a fee and costs," he said, "let's just forget it. Let's say that I finally had a chance to do something, even if it wasn't final, for sons of two fine old men. They would have been proud of you, as I am. Standing up for your rights is sometimes the most difficult thing to do, but in the long run, that posture pays dividends for all people in this country."

EPILOGUE

And so Cricket left Carson and journeyed back to Sierraville.

Before too long, Uncle Bill passed away. And so had the beautiful Ayrab.

Despite all the adversity, Maria and Cricket spent much time together and grew closer and closer.

After the unpleasant events were over, Ramon accepted Cricket as a brother, and the two became fast friends forever. It was Harry Iverson, Ramon's superior at the mill, who had formed the group of rowdies who assaulted Cricket. But

Iverson was acting at the behest of Whipple and Aiken and their cronies. Ramon had gone along as a misguided patriot, never expecting that his sister was so close to the person he was attacking.

Cricket finally proposed to Maria, and they had a beautiful marriage in the same old Catholic Church where John D. had his funeral mass.

Old Manuel gave his simple farm to Ramon, and with no arm-twisting at all, he moved in with the newlyweds on Cricket's farm until the day he passed away.

Maria and Cricket soon had a boy child. Cricket insisted that he be named Bill after his good Uncle and after Bill Kearney, the lawyer who had so faithfully served his family.

In later years, after he had three children by Maria, Cricket was asked to return to the Stewart Indian School, holding down an unlikely combination of jobs – head of the school dairy and also as an assistant coach in the athletic department.

It wasn't long before his coaching skills predominated, and more and more, he worked with the Stewart boxing team. Before he left Stewart, now no longer a militaristic enclave, Cricket had built the Braves into one of the finest amateur boxing teams in America, rivaled mainly by the fabled L. A. Young team from Oakland, California, which spawned any number of professional champions.

Ira, like his father before him, had a political bent, and it was not too long before he ran successfully for an Assembly seat and then for the position of full Senator from Ormsby County, largely constituted of Carson City and its surroundings.

The irony of the situation was that Ira, in a continuation of the role he had always played for Cricket, became the creator and protector of rights in the legislative halls. They had many a chuckle about that.

As previously stated, it was not until 1924, with the passage by Congress of the Indian Rights Act, that Indians were granted full citizenship, and at least theoretically, because some States stalled on one prejudicial ground or another, Indians were given the right to vote for the first time in American history.

Ira and Cricket met at Hallelujah Junction, near Bordertown, and lifted a toast (still illegal for Cricket) to the Indian people, knowing full well that the two of them played a pivotal role in the cruel events leading to a national response to the plight of the Indians.

Other than not being able to purchase and consume alcohol in bars, taverns or liquor stores, a wrong which was finally corrected in 1945 – a "gift" to Indian servicemen who had either given their lives for their country or otherwise stood in harm's way – the Indian was at long last recognized as being "citizen enough" to cast a ballot in federal elections after 1924.

When the day came that Cricket and Ira could drink together in a Carson City bar, then on that day, they were truly equals. But that really was nothing new to them. After all, they were merely carrying on the traditions of John D. and Black Rock Tom.

The "inscrutable desert" facing Ira and Cricket was now free of all "dust devils."

*

AFTERWORD

For granting permission to do this sequel to *Dust Devils,* the author expresses his gratitude and appreciation to his brother Robert's widow, Joyce, and Bob's children: Bruce, Monique and Kristin. May your husband and father look kindly upon this work!

COLOPHON

This book was typeset in Monticello. When typefounders Binny & Ronaldson originally cut this face in the early part of the nineteenth century it was named "Pica Roman No. 1." Thomas Jefferson admired the face and wrote to Ronaldson expressing his interest. Later the face was revived and re-named "Oxford" in 1892 by the American Typefounders Company. It was again revived when Princeton University Press began production on the complete Jefferson Papers. Princeton and Mergenthaler Linotype Company agreed to jointly redesign the face for machine composition on the Linotype. The new version was named Monticello in honor of Jefferson. In the digital world of 2003, world-renowned type designer Matthew Carter, of Carter & Cone, was commissioned to redraw the face to take advantage of modern typesetting systems. It has now been made available for what is currently, in 2004, the world's most powerful personal computer, the Apple Macintosh G5, which was used to compose the present volume.